CONTENTS

Pedigree®

Published by Pedigree Books Limited

Beech Hill House, Walnut Gardens, Exeter, Devon EX4 4DH.

E-mail books@pedigreegroup.co.uk

Published 2005

£7.99

MEET YOUR POKéMON PALS

ASH™

Ash Ketchum is a bit older, a bit wiser, and still determined to become the ultimate Pokémon Master. He's hoping that the Hoenn gym circuit will be the league where he finally reaches first place.

PIKACHU™

Pikachu is Ash's best friend and is by his side in all their adventures. Pikachu is an electric-type Pokémon and can unleash 10,000-volt blasts in battle!

BROCK™

This skilful Pokémon breeder is one of Ash's closest friends. His knowledge, patience and good sense are vital to Ash – as are his amazing cooking skills!

MAY™

May has a passion for seeing new people, new places – and new Pokémon.

MAX™

May's little brother knows so many facts about Pokémon that he's like a walking Pokédex!

TEAM ROCKET™

Jessie, James and Meowth are as fumbling and bumbling as ever. But their boss, Giovanni, has secret plans for the region – so they'd better watch out!

TEAM AQUA™

This evil underworld group is a great threat to Ash and his friends.

TEAM MAGMA™

A menacing underground force that is ready to fight anyone who enters the Hoenn region.

POKé BALL™

There are many kinds of Pokéball, designed for capturing different types of Pokémon in different stages of battle. A good Pokémon trainer will know them all – and when to use them!

POKéDEX™

You won't get far without a Pokédex to give you all the information you need about Pokémon. It's an essential part of any trainer's kit!

THE STORY SO FAR...

As Ash, May, Max, and Brock travel deeper into the wilds of the Hoenn Region, they face a world full of wonders and challenges. Their journeys bring them face to face with a conflict shaking the region to its roots - the battle between the evil forces of Team Aqua and Team Magma. Ash and friends will need all their new skills and Pokémon allies to overcome these two forces and their diabolical plots.

1 TREECKO

Category: Wood Gecko
Type: Grass
Attacks: Pound, Leer, Absorb, Quick Attack, Pursuit, Screech, Mega Drain, Agility, Slam, Detect, Giga Drain
Evolution: >Grovyle >Sceptile
Height: 0.5m/1'8"
Weight: 5kg/11lb

2 GROVYLE

Category: Wood Gecko
Type: Grass
Attacks: Pound, Leer, Absorb, Quick Attack, Fury Cutter, Pursuit, Screech, Leaf Blade, Agility, Slam, Detect, False Swipe
Evolution: >Sceptile
Height: 0.9m/2'11"
Weight: 21.6kg/48lb

3 SCEPTILE

Category: Forest
Type: Grass
Attacks: Pound, Leer, Absorb, Quick Attack, Fury Cutter, Pursuit, Screech, Leaf Blade, Agility, Slam, Detect, False Swipe
Evolution: None
Height: 1.7m/5'7"
Weight: 52.2kg/115lb

4 TORCHIC

Category: Chick
Type: Fire
Attacks: Scratch, Growl, Focus Energy,Ember, Peck, Sand Attack, Fire Spin, Quick Attack, Slash, Mirror Move, Flamethrower
Evolution: >Combusken> Blaziken
Height: 0.4m/1'4"
Weight: 2.5kg/6lb

5 COMBUSKEN

Category: Young Fowl
Type: Fire/Fighting
Attacks: Scratch, Growl, Focus Energy, Ember, Double Kick, Peck, Sand Attack, Bulk Up, Quick Attack, Slash, Mirror Move, Sky Uppercut
Evolution: >Blaziken
Height: 0.9m/2'11'
Weight: 19.5kg/43lb

6 BLAZIKEN

Category: Blaze
Type: Fire/Fighting
Attacks: Fire Punch, Scratch, Growl, Focus Energy, Ember, Double Kick, Peck, Sand Attack, Bulk Up, Quick Attack, Blaze Kick, Slash, Mirror Move, Sky Uppercut
Evolution: None
Height: 1.9m/6'3"
Weight: 52kg/115lb

7 MUDKIP

Category: Mud Fish
Type: Water
Attacks: Tackle, Growl, Mud Slap, Water Gun, Bide, Foresight, Mud Sport, Take Down, Whirlpool, Protect, Hydro Pump, Endeavour
Evolution:>Marshtomp>Swampert
Height: 0.4m/1'4"
Weight: 7.6kg/17lb

8 MARSHTOMP

Category: Mud Fish
Type: Water/Ground
Attacks: Tackle, Growl, Mudslap, Water Gun, Bide, Mud Shot, Foresight, Mud Sport, Take Down, Muddy Water, Protect, Earthquake, Endeavour
Evolution: >Swampert
Height: 0.7m/2'4"
Weight: 28kg/62lb

9 SWAMPERT

Category: Mud Fish
Type: Water/Ground
Attacks: Tackle, Growl, Mudslap, Water Gun, Bide, Mud Shot, Foresight, Mud Sport, Take Down, Muddy Water, Protect, Earthquake, Endeavour
Evolution: None
Height: 1.5m/4'11"
Weight: 81.9kg/181lb

10 POOCHYENA

Category: Bite
Type: Dark
Attacks: Tackle, Howl, Sand Attack, Bite, Odour Sleuth, Roar, Swagger, Scary Face, Take Down, Taunt, Crunch, Thief
Evolution: >Mightyena
Height: 0.5m/1'8"
Weight: 13.6kg/30lb

11 MIGHTYENA

Category: Bite
Type: Dark
Attacks: Tackle, Howl, Sand Attack, Bite, Odour Sleuth, Roar, Swagger, Scary Face, Take Down, Taunt, Crunch, Thief
Evolution: None
Height: 1m/3'3"
Weight: 37kg/82lb

16 BEAUTIFLY

Category: Butterfly
Type: Bug/Flying
Attacks: Absorb, Gust, Stun Spore, Morning Sun, Mega Drain, Whirlwind, Giga Drain, Attract, Silver Wind
Evolution: None
Height: 1m/3'3"
Weight: 28.4kg/63lb

12 ZIGZAGOON

Category: Tinyraccoon
Type: Normal
Attacks: Tackle, Growl, Tail Whip, Headbutt, Sand Attack, Odour Sleuth, Mud Sport, Pin Missile, Covet, Flail, Rest, Belly Drum
Evolution: >Linoone
Height: 0.4m/1'4"
Weight: 17.5kg/39lb

17 CASCOON

Category: Cocoon
Type: Bug
Attacks: Harden
Evolution: >Dustox
Height: 0.7m/2'4"
Weight: 11.5kg/25lb

13 LINOONE

Category: Rushing
Type: Normal
Attacks: Tackle, Growl, Tail Whip, Headbutt, Sand Attack, Odour Sleuth, Mud Sport, Fury Swipes, Covet, Slash, Rest, Belly Drum
Evolution: None
Height: 0.5m/1'8"
Weight: 32.5kg/72lb

18 DUSTOX

Category: Toxic Moth
Type: Bug/Poison
Attacks: Confusion, Gust, Protect, Moonlight, Psybeam, Whirlwind, Light Screen, Toxic, Silver Wind
Evolution: None
Height: 1.2m/3'11"
Weight: 31.6kg/70lb

14 WURMPLE

Category: Worm
Type: Bug
Attacks: Tackle, String Shot, Poison Sting
Evolution: >Silcoon >Beautifly OR >Cascoon>Dustox
Height: 0.3m/1'0"
Weight: 3.6kg/8lb

19 LOTAD

Category: Water Weed
Type: Water/Grass
Attacks: Astonish, Growl, Absorb, Nature Power, Mist, Rain Dance, Mega Drain
Evolution: >Lombre >Ludicolo
Height: 0.5m/1'8"
Weight: 2.6kg/6lb

15 SILCOON

Category: Cocoon
Type: Bug
Attacks: Harden
Evolution: >Beautifly
Height: 0.6m/2'0"
Weight: 10kg/22lb

20 LOMBRE

Category: Jolly
Type: Water/Grass
Attacks: Astonish, Growl, Absorb, Nature Power, Fake Out, Fury Swipes, Water Sport, Thief, Uproar, Hydro Pump
Evolution: >Ludicolo
Height: 1.2m/3'11"
Weight: 32.5kg/72lb

21 LUDICOLO

Category: Carefree
Type: Water/Grass
Attacks: Astonish, Growl, Absorb, Nature Power
Evolution: None
Height: 1.5m/4'11"
Weight: 55kg/121lb

26 SWELLOW

Category: Swallow
Type: Normal/Flying
Attacks: Peck, Growl, Focus Energy, Quick Attack, Wing Attack, Double Team, Endeavour, Aerial Ace, Agility
Evolution: None
Height: 0.7m/2'4"
Weight: 19.8kg/44lb

22 SEEDOT

Category: Acorn
Type: Grass
Attacks: Bide, Harden, Growth, Nature Power, Synthesis, Sunny Day, Explosion
Evolution: >Nuzleaf >Shiftry
Height: 0.5m/1'8"
Weight: 4kg/9lb

27 WINGULL

Category: Seagull
Type: Water/Flying
Attacks: Growl, Water Gun, Supersonic, Wing Attack, Mist, Quick Attack, Pursuit, Agility
Evolution: >Pelipper
Height: 0.6m/2'0"
Weight: 9.5kg/21lb

23 NUZLEAF

Category: Wily
Type: Grass/Dark
Attacks: Pound, Harden, Growth, Nature Power, Fake Out, Torment, Faint Attack, Razor Wind, Swagger, Extrasensory
Evolution: >Shiftry
Height: 1m/3'3"
Weight: 28kg/62lb

28 PELIPPER

Category: Water Bird
Type: Water/Flying
Attacks: Growl, Water Gun, Water Sport, Wing Attack, Supersonic, Mist, Protect, Stockpile, Swallow, Spit Up, Hydro Pump
Evolution: None
Height: 1.2m/3'11"
Weight: 28kg/62lb

24 SHIFTRY

Category: Wicked
Type: Grass/Dark
Attacks: Pound, Harden, Growth, Nature Power
Evolution: None
Height: 1.3m/4'3"
Weight: 59.6kg/131lb

29 RALTS

Category: Feeling
Type: Psychic
Attacks: Growl, Confusion, Double Team, Teleport, Calm Mind, Psychic, Imprison, Future Sight, Hypnosis, Dream Eater
Evolution: >Kirlia >Gardevoir
Height: 0.4m/1'4"
Weight: 6.6kg/15lb

25 TAILLOW

Category: Tinyswallow
Type: Normal/Flying
Attacks: Peck, Growl, Focus Energy, Quick Attack, Wing Attack, Double Team, Endeavour, Aerial Ace, Agility
Evolution: >Swellow
Height: 0.3m/1'0"
Weight: 2.3kg/5lb

30 KIRLIA

Category: Emotion
Type: Psychic
Attacks: Growl, Confusion, Double Team, Teleport, Calm Mind, Psychic, Imprison, Future Sight, Hypnosis, Dream Eater
Evolution: >Gardevoir
Height: 0.8m/2'7"
Weight: 20.2kg/45lb

31 GARDEVOIR

Category: Embrace
Type: Psychic
Attacks: Growl, Confusion, Double Team, Teleport, Calm Mind, Psychic, Imprison, Future Sight, Hypnosis, Dream Eater
Evolution: None
Height: 1.6m/5'3"
Weight: 48.4kg/107lb

36 SLAKOTH

Category: Slacker
Type: Normal
Attacks: Scratch, Yawn, Encore, Slack Off, Faint Attack, Amnesia, Covet, Counter, Flail
Evolution: >Vigoroth >Slaking
Height: 0.8m/2'7"
Weight: 24kg/53lb

32 SURSKIT

Category: Pond Skater
Type: Bug/Water
Attacks: Bubble, Quick Attack, Sweet Scent, Water Sport, Bubble Beam, Agility, Mist, Haze
Evolution: >Masquerain
Height: 0.5m/1'8"
Weight: 1.7kg/4lb

37 VIGOROTH

Category: Wild Monkey
Type: Normal
Attacks: Scratch, Focus Energy, Encore, Uproar, Fury Swipes, Endure, Slash, Counter, Focus Punch, Reversal
Evolution: >Slaking
Height: 1.4m/4'7"
Weight: 46.5kg/103lb

33 MASQUERAIN

Category: Eyeball
Type: Bug/Flying
Attacks: Bubble, Quick Attack, Sweet Scent, Water Sport, Gust, Scary Face, Stun Spore, Silver Wind, Whirlwind
Evolution: None
Height: 0.8m/2'7"
Weight: 3.6kg/8lb

38 SLAKING

Category: Lazy
Type: Normal
Attacks: Scratch, Yawn, Encore, Slack Off, Faint Attack, Amnesia, Covet, Swagger, Counter, Flail
Evolution: None
Height: 2m/6'7"
Weight: 130.5kg/288lb

34 SHROOMISH

Category: Mushroom
Type: Grass
Attacks: Absorb, Tackle, Stun Spore, Leech Seed, Mega Drain, Headbutt, Poisonpowder, Growth, Giga Drain, Spore
Evolution: >Breloom
Height: 0.4m/1'4"
Weight: 4.5kg/10lb

39 ABRA

Category: PSI
Type: Psychic
Attacks: Teleport
Evolution: >Kadabra >Alakazam
Height: 0.9m/2'11"
Weight: 19.5kg/43lb

35 BRELOOM

Category: Mushroom
Type: Grass/Fighting
Attacks: Absorb, Tackle, Stun Spore, Leech Seed, Mega Drain, Headbutt, Mach Punch, Counter, Sky Uppercut, Mind Reader, Dynamicpunch
Evolution: None
Height: 1.2m/3'11"
Weight: 39.2kg/86lb

40 KADABRA

Category: PSI
Type: Psychic
Attacks: Teleport, Kinesis, Confusion, Disable, Psybeam, Reflect, Recover, Future Sight, Role Play, Psychic, Trick
Evolution: >Alakazam
Height: 1.3m/4'3"
Weight: 56.5kg/125lb

SEEING DOUBLE

Ash wants a picture of his favourite Pokémon. Can you help him draw a portrait of Pikachu?

USE THE GRID TO COPY THIS PICTURE - THEN COLOUR IT IN.

WORDSEARCH

A naughty Cacnea has mixed up everyone's names in this grid! Can you find and circle them?

- **Pikachu**
- **Ash**
- **May**
- **Max**
- **Brock**
- **Treecko**
- **Torchic**
- **Mudkip**
- **Jessie**
- **James**
- **Meowth**
- **Hoenn**

Q	W	E	P	I	K	A	C	H	U
R	T	Y	I	U	T	C	I	T	O
X	A	M	K	P	R	I	A	W	S
D	F	G	D	H	E	H	J	O	N
B	L	Z	U	X	E	C	C	E	N
R	V	B	M	I	C	R	N	M	E
O	M	Q	S	W	K	O	E	R	O
C	T	S	Y	M	O	T	U	I	H
K	E	O	A	J	A	M	E	S	J
J	P	Y	A	S	D	F	A	G	H

13

MAXXED OUT!

On their way to Fallarbor Town, Ash and his friends stopped at a Pokémon Centre on the banks of a beautiful lake. Nurse Joy was there to greet them. But as they walked in, May's Skitty released itself and started to whizz around in excitement! Everyone started yelling, trying to catch it. At last Max distracted it and May picked it up.

"Keep it down, will you?" shouted a voice. A boy was scowling at them. "All that yelling is annoying!"

"Sorry about that," said Max.

"Just because you have Pokémon doesn't mean you can do whatever you want!" continued the boy. "Get outta here!"

"Max, that's enough!" said Nurse Joy. The angry boy's name was Max too!

"Two Maxes?" May gasped.

"Not for long," snapped the new Max. "Change your name, kid!"

The new Max stormed off and Nurse Joy sighed.
"Go easy on him," she asked. "He loves Pokémon too and he comes here all the time to play with them."
But Max was too angry to want to make up.
Not far away, Team Rocket was camping out in the forest. Jessie, James and Meowth were making a new plot to catch Pikachu.

Later, Max and May were walking by the lake when they saw a Surskit gliding over the surface. As they checked their Pokédex to learn about it, they saw the new Max talking to it.

"What do you wanna play today?" he asked the Surskit. Then he spotted Max and May. Soon the two Maxes were arguing again.

"I can't believe you two are still going at it!" said Ash, walking up to them with Brock. But nothing could stop the arguing Maxes!

From across the lake, Team Rocket was watching them through binoculars. As soon as they saw Surskit, they decided to steal it for their boss. Brock suggested that they let their Pokémon play together. The new Max's eyes opened wide when he saw them all. "I've never seen so many Pokémon in one place before!" he gasped.

"Some day I'm gonna catch my own Pokémon and become the leader of a gym!" said Max. "That's pretty cool," said the new Max as they watched all the Pokémon playing together. It looked as though they were going to make up, but just at that moment Team Rocket jumped out at them!

"Watch out, Pikachu!" gasped Ash.
"We're not here for Pikachu," said Jessie.
"We're here for Surskit!"
James added.
"Treecko, Quick attack!" yelled Ash.
"Pikachu, Thunderbolt now!"
But Treecko's attack missed. Team Rocket held off the Thunderbolt using a shield that looked like an umbrella. Surskit backed away in terror.

Then Skitty sprang through the air and attached itself to Jessie's long hair! Jessie pulled it off, but her hair was a mess. She ran away crying and James and Meowth followed her.
"Guess we don't have to worry about them!" laughed May. But when they turned around to the lake, Sirskit had vanished!
"It must have got scared and run away!" exclaimed Brock. The new Max was terribly upset. He spotted Surskit's tracks leading away from the lake, but suddenly the ground started to tremble. Trees were mown down in front of them. It was Team Rocket in a huge bulldozer!

Team Rocket chased the friends and sent them flying through the air. May and the two Maxes landed in a tree, but Ash and Brock were flung in a different direction.
"Team Rocket'll be back," May warned.
"So we've gotta find your Surskit fast!" added Max.
"None of this would have happened if Surskit and I had been travelling together like you," sighed the new Max.
"I was a little bit jealous. You get to travel all over the place with all of those cool Pokémon."

"I was jealous of *you*!" said Max in surprise. "You've got that really cool Surskit that you love!"

"That's so weird," laughed the new Max. "A couple of jealous Maxes!"

At last they had made up! But then they heard the rumble of Team Rocket's bulldozer ploughing through the forest.

"We've gotta find Surskit – *now*!" May exclaimed.

In another part of the forest, Ash, Pikachu and Brock were crawling out of the ditch where they had landed. Ash sent Taillow to go and look for May and the others.

May and the two Maxes searched for Surskit by a river, knowing how much it liked water. But Team Rocket burst through the trees behind them!

"Know any other wet areas?" yelled Max as they ran.

"There's a spring deep in the forest!" remembered the new Max.

Max led them to the spring. When they reached it, Surskit was there!

"Surskit! Are you ok?" asked Max, leaping into the water beside his friend. May and Max looked around at the beautiful spring. The water was on two different levels, separated by a big rock. Suddenly there was a crash behind them and Team Rocket burst through the trees!

"Seviper, go!" yelled Jessie.

"Cacnea, I choose you!" James shouted.

"Let's battle 'em!" cried the two Maxes together.

High above, Taillow spotted them and raced off to fetch Ash and Brock.

High above, Taillow spotted them and raced off to fetch Ash and Brock. "Poison Tail, Seviper!" Jessie ordered. "Speed Missile, Cacnea!" yelled James. The three friends scattered as Seviper's Poison Tail smashed into the spot where they had been standing. Surskit sped away to avoid Cacnea's attack. Seviper chased Surskit and blasted it. "No!" cried the two Maxes.

"Needle Arm!" shouted James. But Cacnea was stuck in the water – it couldn't swim! James had to return it to the Pokéball. "Seviper, Poison Tail again!" Jessie yelled. Surskit watched in horror as Seviper got ready to attack.

"We've gotta think fast!" shouted the new Max.

"Think you can break that rock?" asked Max, pointing to the rock between the two levels of the pool. "Surskit, break the rock with Water Pulse!" yelled the new Max. Surskit's Water Pulse powered across the spring and smashed into the rock. Water flooded through and swept Team Rocket off their feet!

Jessie rose out of the water. "Give me that Surskit!" she snarled, grabbing it and trying to pull it out of Max's hands.
"Skitty, help me out!" shouted May. Skitty launched itself at Jessie, beating her around the head with its tail and throwing her back into the water!

Suddenly they heard a shout. "We're coming, you guys!" It was Ash and Brock!
"Perfect!" spat Jessie. "A convenient way to catch Pikachu *and* Surskit! Seviper – get 'em!"
"Pikachu, use Thunderbolt!" ordered Ash. But Team Rocket deflected the Thunderbolt again!
"Surskit, Bubble Beam!" yelled Max. The Bubble Beam knocked their shield out of their hands and they were hit by Pikachu's attack. Team Rocket blasted off again!

"That was great, Max," said Ash.
"And your Surskit's amazing too,"
Brock added.
"I think we made a good team!"
said Max, putting his arm around
the new Max's shoulders.
"It's about time you two became
 friends!" grinned Brock.

THE END

41 ALAKAZAM

Category: PSI
Type: Psychic
Attacks: Teleport, Kinesis, Confusion, Disable, Psybeam, Reflect, Recover, Future Sight, Calm Mind, Psychic, Trick
Evolution: None
Height: 1.5m/4'11"
Weight: 48kg/106lb

46 LOUDRED

Category: Big Voice
Type: Normal
Attacks: Pound, Uproar, Astonish, Howl, Supersonic, Stomp, Screech, Roar, Rest, Sleep Talk, Hyper Voice
Evolution: >Exploud
Height: 1m/3'3"
Weight: 40.5kg/89lb

42 NINCADA

Category: Trainee
Type: Bug/Ground
Attacks: Scratch, Harden, Leech Life, Sand Attack, Fury Swipes, Mind Reader, False Swipe, Mud Slap, Metal Claw, Dig
Evolution: >Ninjask >Shedinja
Height: 0.5m/1'8"
Weight: 5.5kg/12lb

47 EXPLOUD

Category: Loud Noise
Type: Normal
Attacks: Pound, Uproar, Astonish, Howl, Supersonic, Stomp,Screech, Hyper Beam, Roar, Rest, Sleep Talk, Hyper Voice
Evolution: None
Height: 1.5m/4'11"
Weight: 84kg/185lb

43 NINJASK

Category: Ninja
Type: Bug/Flying
Attacks: Scratch, Harden, Leech Life, Sand Attack, Fury Swipes, Mind Reader, Double Team, Fury Cutter, Screech, Swords Dance, Slash, Agility, Baton Pass
Evolution: >Shedinja
Height: 0.8m/2'7"
Weight: 12kg/26lb

48 MAKUHITA

Category: Guts
Type: Fighting
Attacks: Tackle, Focus Energy, Sand Attack, Arm Thrust, Vital Throw, Fake Out, Whirlwind, Knock Off, Smellingsalt, Belly Drum, Endure, Seismic Toss, Reversal
Evolution: >Hariyama
Height: 1m/3'3"
Weight: 86.4kg/191lb

44 SHEDINJA

Category: Shed
Type: Bug/Ghost
Attacks: Scratch, Harden, Leech Life, Sand Attack, Fury Swipes, Mind Reader, Spite, Confuse Ray, Shadow Ball, Grudge
Evolution: None
Height: 0.8m/2'7"
Weight: 1.2kg/3lb

49 HARIYAMA

Category: Arm Thrust
Type: Fighting
Attacks: Tackle, Focus Energy, Sand Attack, Arm Thrust, Vital Throw, Fake Out, Whirlwind, Knock Off, Smellingsalt, Belly Drum, Endure, Seismic Toss, Reversal
Evolution: None
Height: 2.3m/7'7"
Weight: 253.8kg/560lb

45 WHISMUR

Category: Whisper
Type: Normal
Attacks: Pound, Uproar, Astonish, Howl, Supersonic, Stomp, Screech, Roar, Rest, Sleep Talk, Hyper Voice
Evolution: >Loudred >Exploud
Height: 0.6m/2'0"
Weight: 16.3kg/36lb

50 GOLDEEN

Category: Goldfish
Type: Water
Attacks: Peck, Tail Whip, Water Sport, Supersonic, Horn Attack, Flail, Fury Attack, Waterfall, Horn Drill, Agility
Evolution: >Seaking
Height: 0.6m/2'0"
Weight: 15kg/33lb

51 SEAKING

Category: Goldfish
Type: Water
Attacks: Peck, Tail Whip, Water Sport, Supersonic, Horn Attack, Flail, Fury Attack, Waterfall, Horn Drill, Agility
Evolution: None
Height: 1.3m/4'3"
Weight: 39kg/86lb

52 MAGIKARP

Category: Fish
Type: Water
Attacks: Splash, Tackle, Flail
Evolution: >Gyarados
Height: 0.9m/2'11"
Weight: 10kg/22lb

53 GYARADOS

Category: Atrocious
Type: Water/Flying
Attacks: Thrash, Bite, Dragon Rage, Leer, Twister, Hydro Pump, Rain Dance, Dragon Dance, Hyper Beam
Evolution: None
Height: 6.5m/21'4"
Weight: 235kg/518lb

54 AZURILL

Category: Polka Dot
Type: Normal
Attacks: Splash, Charm, Tail Whip, Bubble, Slam, Water Gun
Evolution: >Marill >Azumarill
Height: 0.2m/0'8"
Weight: 2kg/4lb

55 MARILL

Category: Aquamouse
Type: Water
Attacks: Tackle, Defence Curl, Tail Whip, Water Gun, Rollout, Bubblebeam, Double Edge, Rain Dance, Hydro Pump
Evolution: >Azumarill
Height: 0.4m/1'4"
Weight: 8.5kg/19lb

56 AZUMARILL

Category: Aquarabbit
Type: Water
Attacks: Tackle, Defence Curl, Tail Whip, Water Gun, Rollout, Bubblebeam, Double Edge, Rain Dance, Hydro Pump
Evolution: None
Height: 0.8m/2'7"
Weight: 28.5kg/63lb

57 GEODUDE

Category: Rock
Type: Rock/Ground
Attacks: Tackle, Defence Curl, Mud Sport, Rock Throw, Magnitude, Selfdestruct, Rollout, Rock Blast, Earthquake, Explosion, Double Edge
Evolution: >Graveler >Golem
Height: 0.4m/1'4"
Weight: 20kg/44lb

58 GRAVELER

Category: Rock
Type: Rock/Ground
Attacks: Tackle, Defence Curl, Mud Sport, Rock Throw, Magnitude, Selfdestruct, Rollout, Rock Blast, Earthquake, Explosion, Double Edge
Evolution: >Golem
Height: 1m/3'3"
Weight: 105kg/232lb

59 GOLEM

Category: Megaton
Type: Rock/Ground
Attacks: Tackle, Defence Curl, Mud Sport, Rock Throw, Magnitude, Selfdestruct, Rollout, Rock Blast, Earthquake, Explosion, Double Edge
Evolution: None
Height: 1.4m/4'7"
Weight: 300kg/662lb

60 NOSEPASS

Category: Compass
Type: Rock
Attacks: Tackle, Harden, Rock Throw, Block, Thunder Wave, Rock Slide, Sandstorm, Rest, Zap Cannon, Lock On
Evolution: None
Height: 1m/3'3"
Weight: 97kg/214lb

61 SKITTY

Category: Kitten
Type: Normal
Attacks: Growl, Tackle, Tail Whip, Sing, Doubleslap, Attract, Assist, Charm, Faint Attack, Covet, Heal Bell, Double Edge
Evolution: >Delcatty
Height: 0.6m/2'0"
Weight: 11kg/24lb

66 TENTACOOL

Category: Jellyfish
Type: Water/Poison
Attacks: Poison Sting, Supersonic, Constrict, Acid, Bubblebeam, Wrap, Barrier, Screech, Hydro Pump
Evolution: >Tentacruel
Height: 0.9m/2'11"
Weight: 45.5kg/100lb

62 DELCATTY

Category: Prim
Type: Normal
Attacks: Growl, Sing, Attract, Doubleslap
Evolution: None
Height: 1.1m/3'7"
Weight: 32.6kg/72lb

67 TENTACRUEL

Category: Jellyfish
Type: Water/Poison
Attacks: Poison Sting, Supersonic, Constrict, Acid, Bubblebeam, Wrap, Barrier, Screech, Hydro Pump
Evolution: None
Height: 1.6m/5'3"
Weight: 55kg/121lb

63 ZUBAT

Category: Bat
Type: Poison/Flying
Attacks: Leech Life, Supersonic, Astonish, Bite, Wing Attack, Confuse Ray, Air Cutter, Mean Look, Poison Fang, Haze
Evolution: >Golbat >Crobat
Height: 0.8m/2'7"
Weight: 7.5kg/17lb

68 SABLEYE

Category: Darkness
Type: Dark/Ghost
Attacks: Leer, Scratch, Foresight, Night Shade, Astonish, Fury Swipes, Fake Out, Detect, Faint Attack, Knock Off, Confuse Ray, Shadow Ball, Mean Look
Evolution: None
Height: 0.5m/1'8"
Weight: 11kg/24lb.

64 GOLBAT

Category: Bat
Type: Poison/Flying
Attacks: Screech, Leech Life, Supersonic, Astonish, Bite, Wing Attack, Confuse Ray, Air Cutter, Mean Look, Poison Fang, Haze
Evolution: >Crobat
Height: 1.6m/5'3"
Weight: 55kg/121lb

69 MAWILE

Category: Deceiver
Type: Steel
Attacks: Astonish, Fake Tears, Bite, Sweet Scent, Vicegrip, Faint Attack, Baton Pass, Crunch, Iron Defence, Stockpile, Swallow, Spit Up
Evolution: None
Height: 0.6m/2'0"
Weight: 11.5kg/25lb

65 CROBAT

Category: Bat
Type: Poison/Flying
Attacks: Screech, Leech Life, Supersonic, Astonish, Bite, Wing Attack, Confuse Ray, Air Cutter, Mean Look, Poison Fang, Haze
Evolution: None
Height: 1.8m/5'11"
Weight: 75kg/165lb

70 ARON

Category: Iron Armour
Type: Steel/Rock
Attacks: Tackle, Harden, Mud Slap, Headbutt, Metal Claw, Iron Defence, Roar, Take Down, Iron Tail, Protect, Metal Sound, Double Edge
Evolution: >Lairon >Aggron
Height: 0.4m/1'4"
Weight: 60kg/132lb

71 LAIRON

Category: Iron Armour
Type: Steel/Rock
Attacks: Tackle, Harden, Mud Slap, Headbutt, Metal Claw, Iron Defence, Roar, Take Down, Iron Tail, Protect, Metal Sound, Double Edge
Evolution: >Aggron
Height: 0.9m/2'11"
Weight: 120kg/265lb

72 AGGRON

Category: Iron Armour
Type: Steel/Rock
Attacks: Tackle, Harden, Mud Slap, Headbutt, Metal Claw, Iron Defence, Roar, Take Down, Iron Tail, Protect, Metal Sound, Double Edge
Evolution: None
Height: 2.1m/6'11"
Weight: 360kg/794lb

73 MACHOP

Category: Superpower
Type: Fighting
Attacks: Low Kick, Leer, Focus Energy, Karate Chop, Seismic Toss, Foresight, Revenge, Vital Throw, Submission, Cross Chop, Scary Face, Dynamicpunch
Evolution: >Machoke >Machamp
Height: 0.8m/2'7"
Weight: 19.5kg/43lb

74 MACHOKE

Category: Superpower
Type: Fighting
Attacks: Low Kick, Leer, Focus Energy, Karate Chop, Seismic Toss, Foresight, Revenge, Vital Throw, Submission, Cross Chop, Scary Face, Dynamicpunch
Evolution: >Machamp
Height: 1.5m/4'11"
Weight: 70.5kg/155lb

75 MACHAMP

Category: Superpower
Type: Fighting
Attacks: Low Kick, Leer, Focus Energy, Karate Chop, Seismic Toss, Foresight, Revenge, Vital Throw, Submission, Cross Chop, Scary Face, Dynamicpunch
Evolution: None
Height: 1.6m/5'3"
Weight: 130kg/287lb

76 MEDITITE

Category: Meditate
Type: Fighting/Psychic
Attacks: Bide, Meditate, Confusion, Detect, Hidden Power, Mind Reader, Calm Mind, Hi Jump Kick, Psych Up, Reversal, Recover
Evolution: >Medicham
Height: 0.6m/2'0"
Weight: 11.2kg/25lb

77 MEDICHAM

Category: Meditate
Type: Fighting/Psychic
Attacks: Fire Punch, Thunderpunch, Ice Punch, Bide, Meditate, Confusion, Detect, Hidden Power, Mind Reader, Calm Mind, Hi Jump Kick, Psych Up, Reversal, Recover
Evolution: >None
Height: 1.3m/4'3"
Weight: 31.5kg/69lb

78 ELECTRIKE

Category: Lightning
Type: Electric
Attacks: Tackle, Thunder Wave, Leer, Howl, Quick Attack, Spark, Odour Sleuth, Roar, Bite, Thunder, Charge
Evolution: >Manectric
Height: 0.6m/2'0"
Weight: 15.2kg/34lb

79 MANECTRIC

Category: Discharge
Type: Electric
Attacks: Tackle, Thunder Wave, Leer, Howl, Quick Attack, Spark, Odour Sleuth, Roar, Bite, Thunder, Charge
Evolution: None
Height: 1.5m/4'11"
Weight: 40.2kg/89lb

80 PLUSLE

Category: Cheering
Type: Electric
Attacks: Growl, Thunder Wave, Quick Attack, Helping Hand, Spark, Encore, Fake Tears, Charge, Thunder, Baton Pass, Agility
Evolution: None
Height: 0.4m/1'4"
Weight: 4.2kg/9lb

EVOLUTION EXAM

Are you a dedicated Pokémon trainer? If you want to reach the championship tournament, like Ash, you need to know your Pokémon!

Can you match the Pokémon on the left to the Pokémon they will evolve into?

1. Geodude

2. Lileep

3. Oddish

4. Staryu

5. Wurmple

A. Cradily

B. Starmie

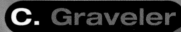

C. Graveler

D. Silcoon

E. Gloom

36

THE GREAT ESCAPE

Team Magma have joined forces with Team Rocket to attack Ash and steal Pikachu! Can you help Ash and Pikachu reach their friends without getting caught?

PROS AND CON ARTISTS!

At last Ash and his friends arrived in Fallarbor Town. May was very excited because she was going to enter her second Pokémon contest. She wanted to show that she and Beautifly had got what it took to win! Max laughed at her for dreaming of winning first prize, but she turned on him angrily. "If I'm not gonna believe in myself then who will?" she argued.
"That's the spirit," grinned Ash.
But when they arrived at the Pokémon Centre they realised that May was going to have some tough competition – there were some really good trainers there!

The friends met a trainer called Grace, who had an amazing Medicham Pokémon. She had already won three ribbons and May's confidence drained away. Grace tried to comfort her.

"It's not always the coordinator with the most experience that wins," she said. "Who your opponent is has a lot to do with it, and sometimes it's just luck. But you'll never be able to win until you can use the power of your Pokémon completely."

May still felt worried that she wasn't good enough, so Grace showed her how to do a combination attack. But when May tried it with Beautifly it went wrong. Someone behind her started to laugh. It was Drew, an arrogant trainer they had met before.
"A coordinator with no ribbons at all really doesn't stand a chance in a competition like this!" he smirked.

Meanwhile, Team Rocket was up to no good in Fallarbor Town. They had painted some ordinary Pokéblock gold and silver. They were selling it to trainers, telling them it would make their Pokémon win the contest!

Later that day Drew challenged Ash to a battle. Ash chose Taillow and Drew chose Roselia.

"Quick attack!" ordered Ash.

"Roselia – Magical Leaf!" Drew shouted. Taillow dodged the attack and launched a Peck attack.

"Stun Spore!" cried Drew.

"Climb and Dodge!" Ash yelled, and Taillow sped into the sky. But it couldn't avoid the attack and was hit, just as May ran up. Taillow crashed to the ground and the victory went to Drew. May lost even more confidence when she saw Ash lose. If *he* couldn't win – how could *she*?

Next day Team Rocket was in disguise, selling fake Pokéblock. May wandered up to their stall and listened to what people were saying about the miracle Pokéblock.
She even started to wonder if it would help Beautifly. But before she could buy any, Grace walked up, looking angry.
"Just what exactly is your magical Pokéblock made of?" she asked.
Team Rocket couldn't answer!

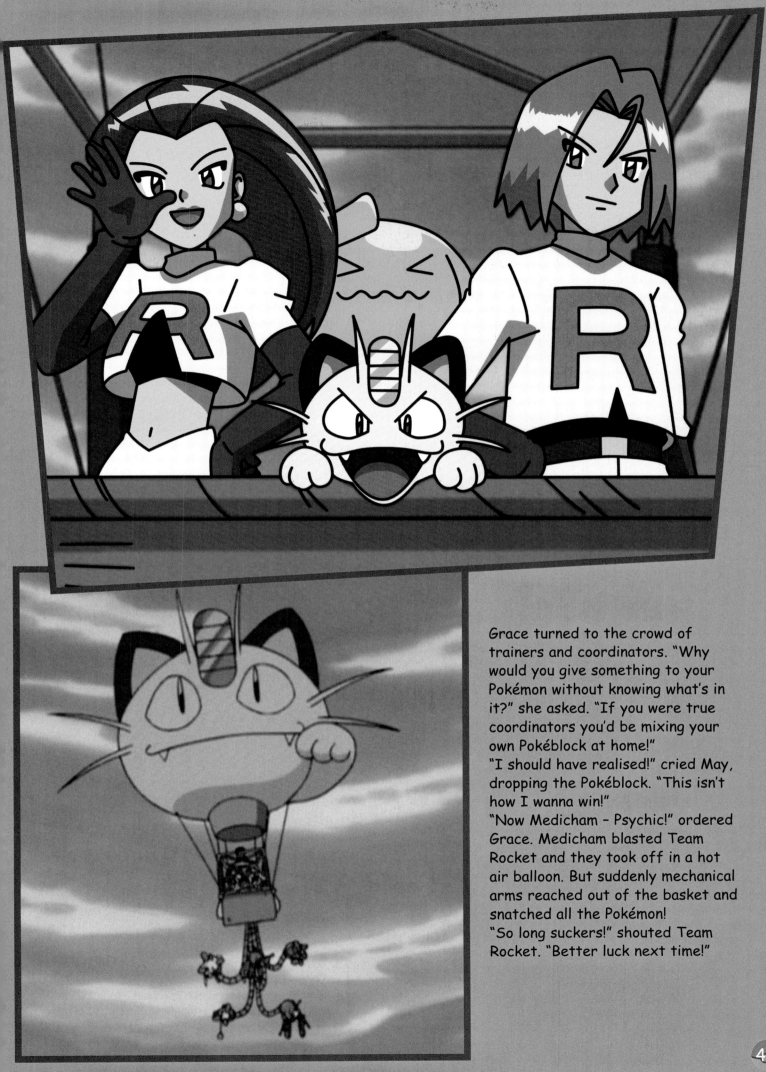

Grace turned to the crowd of trainers and coordinators. "Why would you give something to your Pokémon without knowing what's in it?" she asked. "If you were true coordinators you'd be mixing your own Pokéblock at home!"

"I should have realised!" cried May, dropping the Pokéblock. "This isn't how I wanna win!"

"Now Medicham – Psychic!" ordered Grace. Medicham blasted Team Rocket and they took off in a hot air balloon. But suddenly mechanical arms reached out of the basket and snatched all the Pokémon!

"So long suckers!" shouted Team Rocket. "Better luck next time!"

But Grace wasn't beaten yet! "Go Medicham – Psychic!" she yelled. Medicham's energy burst made the mechanical arms drop the Pokémon. "Beautifly, String Shot – go!" shouted May. Beautifly attached a string to the balloon and stopped Team Rocket leaving. James's Cacnea cut the string and Jessie released her Seviper.
"Poison Tail!" she ordered. "Medicham – Ice Punch!" Grace yelled. Cacnea and Seviper were flung back and Team Rocket blasted off again!

The contest started the next day, and May did well in the first round. Ash, Brock and Max were cheering her on in the crowd. But then a mysterious contestant called Jessica came in. With her Dustox Pokémon she did amazing tricks and impressed the judges. No one had ever seen a contestant like Jessica before. But backstage, James and Meowth were helping her cheat on all the tricks – Jessica was Jessie in disguise!

Jessica, Grace, Drew and May all got through to the second round. May had to battle Jessica! They fought a powerful battle with Beautifly and Dustox. But then something went wrong with Meowth's controls. Jessica lost all her points and May was through to the final! The electronic control device fell off Dustox and the crowd realised it had all been a trick! They started to boo Jessica. She pulled off her disguise and Ash saw that it was Jessie! Meowth and James came out to join her. "We're taking all your Pokémon!" shouted Meowth. "No you're not!" cried Ash. "Pikachu – Thunderbolt!" Pikachu hit them with a powerful attack and Team Rocket blasted off again!

Next it was time for Grace to
battle Drew.
"Drew against Grace – that should be good!"
grinned Ash.
"Yeah, they're both pretty tough,"
Max agreed.
Grace and Drew fought a mighty battle,
using awesome combination attacks and
lightning-fast strategies. But at last
Medicham scored a direct hit on Roselia
with a High Jump Kick and Drew lost
all his points.
"Medicham, you were great!" grinned Grace.
"Roselia, you were awesome, what a great
show!" Drew smiled.
But May's confidence was shaken. "If Grace
can beat Drew like that, how will I beat
her?" she wondered.

As May and Grace faced each other for the final victory battle, May was determined to do her best.

"Don't think for a second that I'll be holding back, May," said Grace.

"I've worked hard to get to this point!" said May.

"I will not lose! Beautifly, Tackle now!"

"Medicham, dodge!" shouted Grace. Medicham attacked with Ice Punch but Beautifly reacted with Gust attack – right on target! Medicham was hit and Grace lost points.

"Awesome!" shouted Max.

"It's not over yet!" cried Grace.

Medicham used confusion to tangle Beautifly in its own String Shot and followed it up with another Ice Punch. The judges were impressed and May lost points. Beautifly broke free at last and launched into a Tackle and String Shot combination. "May must have learnt that watching Grace's strategy!" Ash grinned. "Medicham – Confusion!" Grace ordered. Medicham stopped the attack, but Beautifly went into a spin and captured Medicham in a silver tornado! "Tackle attack now!" yelled May. Medicham fell to the ground.

"Now we can finish this up!" yelled May. "Tackle and Silver Wind!" Beautifly's intense attack combination made Medicham lose even more points!

"May's gonna win!" whooped Max.

"This battle's just begun!" Grace yelled. "Medicham – High Jump Kick!"

"Beautifly, Tackle!" shouted May. Beautifly and Medicham met in a head-to-head collision and both fell to the floor.

But May had more points left – she was the winner of the Fallarbor competition!

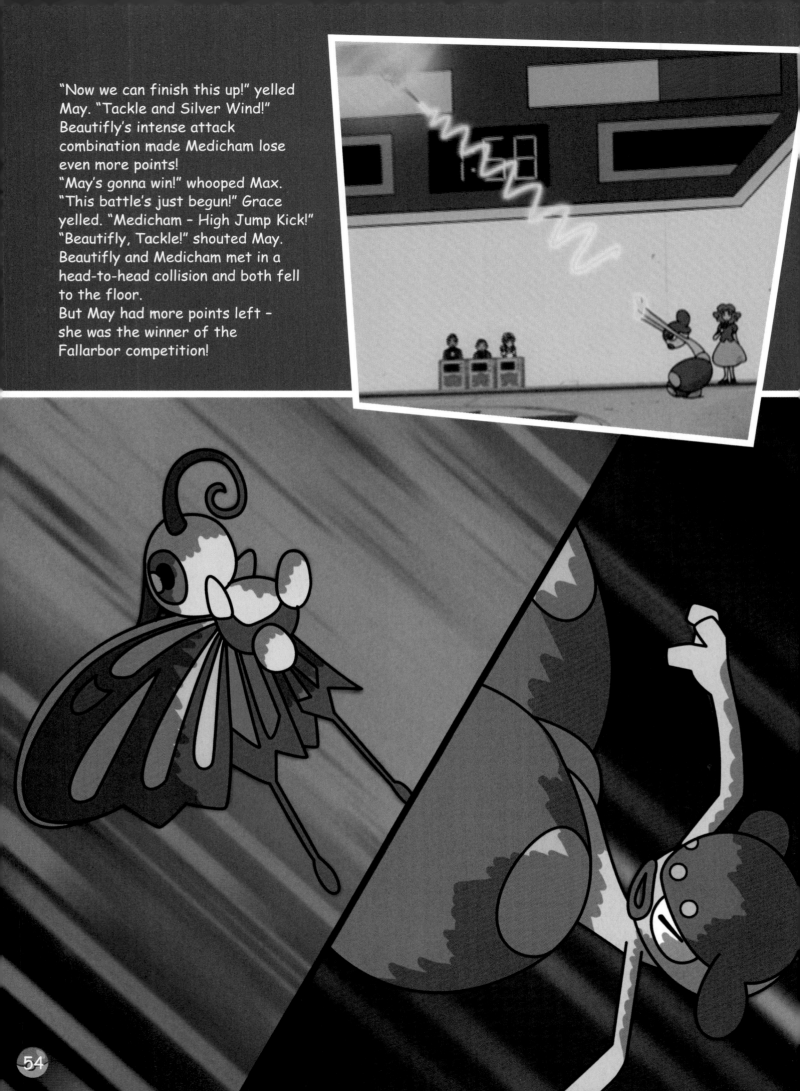

54

"That was a great battle," Grace told May. "I'm impressed."
"Thanks, but I owe my victory to you," May smiled.
"You fought and won," laughed Grace. "Have a little bit more confidence!"
May was really excited about winning her first ribbon. Her friends were very proud of her as they headed for Lavaridge Town and the next gym battle.

THE END

MASTER OR MENACE

Do you belong with Ash and Brock, or would you struggle to keep up with Jessie and James? Check out your skills with this quiz, and discover whether you're a Pokémon master or a menace to society!

1. **What sort of Pokéball would you use against Bug and Water type Pokémon?**
a. A Net Ball.
b. A Premier Ball.
c. Whichever one I grab first.

2. **Your Pokémon is ill and needs treatment. But you have an important gym battle to fight. Do you ...**
a. Forget the battle – your Pokémon friend is more important?
b. Hope that your Pokémon will last until the end of the battle?
c. Ignore it – your Pokémon has to have stamina?

3. **Why are you training Pokémon and fighting gym battles?**
a. To meet new friends and become the greatest Pokémon Master ever!
b. Pokémon are kinda cute, and I love the travelling.
c. To destroy the other teams any way I can.

4. **What does a Torchic evolve into first?**
a. Combusken.
b. Blaziken.
c. Marshtomp.

5. **What do you do with your Pokémon when you enter a new region?**
a. Leave them behind – I want to make a fair and fresh start.
b. Take a few with me – I worked hard to catch them!
c. Take them with me – I need all the help I can get in this new region!

6. You are walking through a wood when a Duskull Pokémon appears next to you. Do you ...
a. Try to catch it with a Pokeball?
b. Scream your head off and run away?
c. Use your most powerful Pokémon to attack it – you'll teach it to scare you?

7. My Pokédex is ...
a. Essential.
b. Handy – when I remember to check it.
c. Lost.

8. Your Pokémon are ...
a. Friends.
b. A bit of a worry.
c. Servants.

9. You meet a nasty Pokémon trainer who makes fun of you and says she can't be beaten. Do you ...
a. Get ready to battle and ignore her childish teasing?
b. Get ready to battle but worry that you can't win?
c. Get ready to run away?

10. Ninetales is ...
a. A Fire-type Pokémon.
b. An Electric-type Pokémon.
c. A storybook.

Results

Mostly As: Ash and Brock would welcome you! You've got excellent knowledge of your Pokémon and you make a great friend you must sleep with your Pokédex under your pillow!

Mostly Bs: You mean well but you still make mistakes – but don't worry because so do May and Max! Study your Pokédex a bit harder and try again.

Mostly Cs: Uh-oh. Call yourself a Pokémon trainer? Have you ever looked at your Pokédex? Better join Team Rocket – if they'll have you!

ODD POKÉMON OUT

Team Rocket is up to its old tricks again! Jessie and James have disguised themselves as different Pokémon to sneak up on Ash, but they haven't got it quite right. Can you spot the odd one out in each group to find that pesky trio?

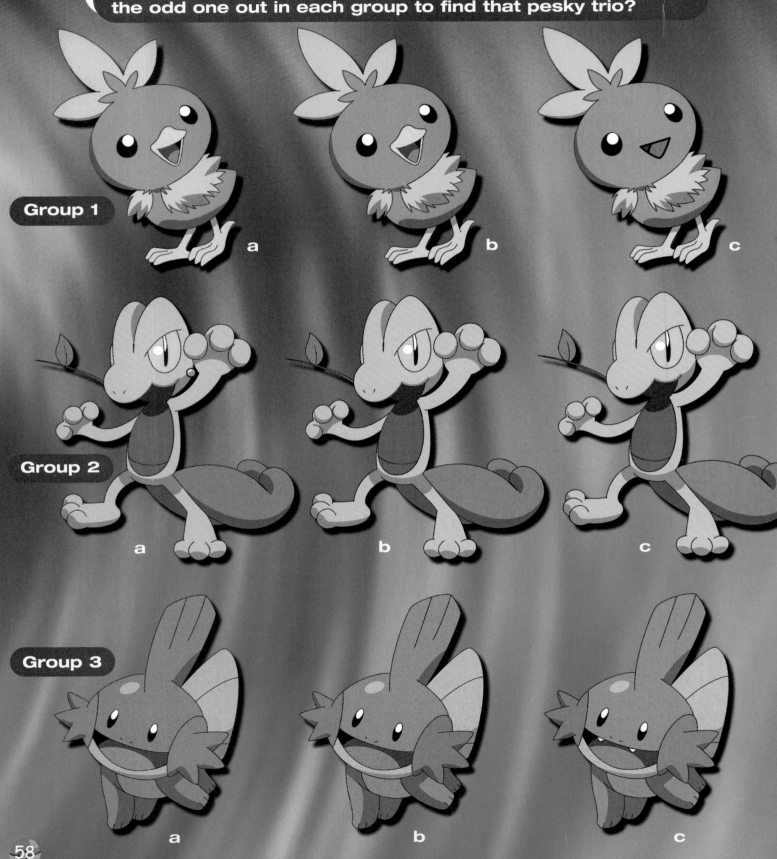

Group 1

a

b

c

Group 2

a

b

c

Group 3

a

b

c

CROSSWORD

Across

1. What is the name of Ash's first Pokémon?
7. Which team does Jessie belong to?
8. What is the type of an Exploud Pokémon?
10. What is the type of a Mudkip Pokémon?

Down

2. What is the category of a Torchic Pokémon?
3. What do you use to catch a Pokémon?
4. What does a Natu Pokémon evolve into?
5. What is the type of a Treecko Pokémon?
6. What does a Swellow Pokémon evolve from?
9. What is the name of May's little brother?

81 MINUN

Category: Cheering
Type: Electric
Attacks: Growl, Thunder Wave, Quick Attack, Helping Hand, Spark, Encore, Charm, Charge, Thunder, Baton Pass, Agility
Evolution: None
Height: 0.4m/1'4"
Weight: 4.2kg/9lb

86 VOLBEAT

Category: Firefly
Type: Bug
Attacks: Tackle, Confuse Ray, Double Team, Moonlight, Quick Attack, Tail Glow, Signal Beam, Protect, Helping Hand, Double Edge
Evolution: None
Height: 0.7m/2'4"
Weight: 17.7kg/39lb

82 MAGNEMITE

Category: Magnet
Type: Electric/Steel
Attacks: Metal Sound, Tackle, Thundershock, Supersonic, Sonicboom, Thunder Wave, Spark, Lock On, Swift, Screech, Zap Cannon
Evolution: >Magneton
Height: 0.3m/1'0"
Weight: 6kg/13lb

87 ILLUMISE

Category: Firefly
Type: Bug
Attacks: Tackle, Sweet Scent, Charm, Moonlight, Quick Attack, Wish, Encore, Flatter, Helping Hand, Covet
Evolution: None
Height: 0.6m/2'0"
Weight: 17.7kg/39lb

83 MAGNETON

Category: Magnet
Type: Electric/Steel
Attacks: Metal Sound, Tackle, Thundershock, Supersonic, Sonicboom, Thunder Wave, Spark, Lock On, Tri Attack, Screech, Zap Cannon
Evolution: None
Height: 1m/3'3"
Weight: 60kg/132lb

88 ODDISH

Category: Weed
Type: Grass/Poison
Attacks: Absorb, Sweet Scent, Poisonpowder, Stun Spore, Sleep Powder, Acid, Moonlight, Petal Dance
Evolution: > Gloom >Vileplume >Bellossom
Height: 0.5m/1'8"
Weight: 5.4kg/12lb

84 VOLTORB

Category: Ball
Type: Electric
Attacks: Charge, Tackle, Screech, Sonicboom, Spark, Selfdestruct, Rollout, Light Screen, Swift, Explosion, Mirror Coat
Evolution: >Electrode
Height: 0.5m/1'8"
Weight: 10.4kg/23lb

89 GLOOM

Category: Weed
Type: Grass/Poison
Attacks: Absorb, Sweet Scent, Poisonpowder, Stun Spore, Sleep Powder, Acid, Moonlight, Petal Dance
Evolution: >Vileplume >Bellossom
Height: 0.8m/2'7"
Weight: 8.6kg/19lb

85 ELECTRODE

Category: Ball
Type: Electric
Attacks: Charge, Tackle, Screech, Sonicboom, Spark, Selfdestruct, Rollout, Light Screen, Swift, Explosion, Mirror Coat
Evolution: None
Height: 1.2m/3'11"
Weight: 66.6kg/147lb

90 VILEPLUME

Category: Flower
Type: Grass/Poison
Attacks: Absorb, Aromatherapy, Stun Spore, Mega Drain, Petal Dance
Evolution: >Bellossom
Height: 1.2m/3'11"
Weight: 18.6kg/41lb

91 BELLOSSOM

Category: Flower
Type: Grass
Attacks: Absorb, Sweet Scent, Stun Spore, Magical Leaf, Petal Dance, Solarbeam
Evolution: None
Height: 0.4m/1'4"
Weight: 5.8kg/13lb

92 DODUO

Category: Twin Bird
Type: Normal/Flying
Attacks: Peck, Growl, Pursuit, Fury Attack, Tri Attack, Rage, Uproar, Drill Peck, Agility
Evolution: >Dodrio
Height: 1.4m/4'7"
Weight: 39.2kg/86lb

93 DODRIO

Category: Triple Bird
Type: Normal/Flying
Attacks: Peck, Growl, Pursuit, Fury Attack, Tri Attack, Rage, Uproar, Drill Peck, Agility
Evolution: None
Height: 1.8m/5'11"
Weight: 85.2kg/188lb

94 ROSELIA

Category: Thorn
Type: Grass/Poison
Attacks: Absorb, Growth, Poison Sting, Stun Spore, Mega Drain, Leech Seed, Magical Leaf, Grasswhistle, Giga Drain, Sweet Scent, Ingrain, Toxic, Petal Dance, Aromatherapy, Synthesis
Evolution: None
Height: 0.3m/1'0"
Weight: 2kg/4lb

95 GULPIN

Category: Stomach
Type: Poison
Attacks: Pound, Yawn, Poison Gas, Sludge, Amnesia, Encore, Toxic, Stockpile, Spit Up, Swallow, Sludge Bomb
Evolution: >Swalot
Height: 0.4m/1'4"
Weight: 10.3kg/23lb

96 SWALOT

Category: Poison Bag
Type: Poison
Attacks: Pound, Yawn, Poison Gas, Sludge, Amnesia, Encore, Body Slam, Toxic, Stockpile, Spit Up, Swallow, Sludge Bomb
Evolution: None
Height: 1.7m/5'7"
Weight: 80kg/176lb

97 CARVANHA

Category: Savage
Type: Water/Dark
Attacks: Leer, Bite, Rage, Focus Energy, Scary Face, Crunch, Screech, Take Down, Swagger, Agility
Evolution: >Sharpedo
Height: 0.8m/2'7"
Weight: 20.8kg/46lb

98 SHARPEDO

Category: Brutal
Type: Water/Dark
Attacks: Leer, Bite, Rage, Focus Energy, Scary Face, Crunch, Screech, Slash, Taunt, Swagger, Skull Bash, Agility
Evolution: None
Height: 1.8m/5'11"
Weight: 88.8kg/196lb

99 WAILMER

Category: Ball Whale
Type: Water
Attacks: Splash, Growl, Water Gun, Rollout, Whirlpool, Astonish, Water Pulse, Mist, Rest, Water Spout, Amnesia, Hydro Pump
Evolution: >Wailord
Height: 2m/6'7"
Weight: 130kg/287lb

100 WAILORD

Category: Float Whale
Type: Water
Attacks: Splash, Growl, Water Gun, Rollout, Whirlpool, Astonish, Water Pulse, Mist, Rest, Water Spout, Amnesia, Hydro Pump
Evolution: None
Height: 14.5m/47'7"
Weight: 398kg/878lb

101 NUMEL

Category: Numb
Type: Fire/Ground
Attacks: Growl, Tackle, Ember, Magnitude, Focus Energy, Take Down, Amnesia, Earthquake, Flamethrower, Double Edge
Evolution: >Camerupt
Height: 0.7m/2'4"
Weight: 24kg/53lb

102 CAMERUPT

Category: Eruption
Type: Fire/Ground
Attacks: Growl, Tackle, Ember, Magnitude, Focus Energy, Take Down, Amnesia, Rock Slide, Earthquake, Eruption, Fissure
Evolution: None
Height: 1.9m/6'3"
Weight: 220kg/485lb

103 SLUGMA

Category: Lava
Type: Fire
Attacks: Yawn, Smog, Ember, Rock Throw, Harden, Amnesia, Flamethrower, Rock Slide, Body Slam
Evolution: >Magcargo
Height: 0.7m/2'4"
Weight: 35kg/77lb

104 MAGCARGO

Category: Lava
Type: Fire/Rock
Attacks: Yawn, Smog, Ember, Rock Throw, Harden, Amnesia, Flamethrower, Rock Slide, Body Slam
Evolution: None
Height: 0.8m/2'7"
Weight: 55kg/121lb

105 TORKOAL

Category: Coal
Type: Fire
Attacks: Ember, Smog, Curse, Smokescreen, Fire Spin, Body Slam, Protect, Flamethrower, Iron Defence, Amnesia, Flail, Heat Wave
Evolution: None
Height: 0.5m/1'8"
Weight: 80.4kg/177lb

106 GRIMER

Category: Sludge
Type: Poison
Attacks: Poison Gas, Pound, Harden, Disable, Sludge, Minimise, Screech, Acid Armour, Sludge Bomb, Memento
Evolution: >Muk
Height: 0.9m/2'11"
Weight: 30kg/66lb

107 MUK

Category: Sludge
Type: Poison
Attacks: Poison Gas, Pound, Harden, Disable, Sludge, Minimise, Screech, Acid Armour, Sludge Bomb, Memento
Evolution: None
Height: 1.2m/3'11"
Weight: 30kg/66lb

108 KOFFING

Category: Poison Gas
Type: Poison
Attacks: Poison Gas, Tackle, Smog, Selfdestruct, Sludge, Smokescreen, Haze, Explosion, Destiny Bond, Memento
Evolution: >Weezing
Height: 0.6m/2'0"
Weight: 1kg/2lb

109 WEEZING

Category: Poison Gas
Type: Poison
Attacks: Poison Gas, Tackle, Sludge, Smog, Selfdestruct, Smokescreen, Haze, Explosion, Destiny Bond, Memento
Evolution: None
Height: 1.2m/3'11"
Weight: 9.5kg/21lb

110 SPOINK

Category: Bounce
Type: Psychic
Attacks: Splash, Psywave, Odour Sleuth, Psybeam, Psych Up, Confuse Ray, Magic Coat, Psychic, Rest, Snore, Bounce
Evolution: >Grumpig
Height: 0.7m/2'4"
Weight: 30.6kg/67lb

111 GRUMPIG

Category: Manipulate
Type: Psychic
Attacks: Splash, Psywave, Odour Sleuth, Psybeam, Psych Up, Confuse Ray, Magic Coat, Psychic, Rest, Snore, Bounce
Evolution: None
Height: 0.9m/2'11"
Weight: 71.5kg/158lb

112 SANDSHREW

Category: Mouse
Type: Ground
Attacks: Scratch, Defence Curl, Sand Attack, Poison Sting, Slash, Swift, Fury Swipes, Sand Tomb, Sandstorm
Evolution: >Sandslash
Height: 0.6m/2'0"
Weight: 12kg/26lb

113 SANDSLASH

Category: Mouse
Type: Ground
Attacks: Scratch, Defence Curl, Sand Attack, Poison Sting, Slash, Swift, Fury Swipes, Sand Tomb, Sandstorm
Evolution: None
Height: 1m/3'3"
Weight: 29.5kg/65lb

114 SPINDA

Category: Spot Panda
Type: Normal
Attacks: Tackle, Uproar, Faint Attack, Psybeam, Hypnosis, Dizzy Punch, Teeter Dance, Psych Up, Double Edge, Flail, Thrash
Evolution: None
Height: 1.1m/3'7"
Weight: 5kg/11lb

115 SKARMORY

Category: Armor Bird
Type: Steel/Flying
Attacks: Leer, Peck, Sand Attack, Swift, Agility, Fury Attack, Air Cutter, Steel Wing, Spikes, Metal Sound
Evolution: None
Height: 1.7m/5'7"
Weight: 50.5kg/111lb

116 TRAPINCH

Category: Ant Pit
Type: Ground
Attacks: Bite, Sand Attack, Faint Attack, Sand Tomb, Crunch, Dig, Sandstorm, Hyper Beam
Evolution: >Vibrava >Flygon
Height: 0.7m/2'4"
Weight: 15kg/33lb

117 VIBRAVA

Category: Vibration
Type: Ground/Dragon
Attacks: Bite, Sand Attack, Faint Attack, Sand Tomb, Crunch, Dragonbreath, Screech, Sandstorm, Hyper Beam
Evolution: >Flygon
Height: 1.1m/3'7"
Weight: 15.3kg/34lb

118 FLYGON

Category: Mystic
Type: Ground/Dragon
Attacks: Bite, Sand Attack, Faint Attack, Sand Tomb, Crunch, Dragonbreath, Screech, Sandstorm, Hyper Beam
Evolution: None
Height: 2m/6'7"
Weight: 82kg/181lb

119 CACNEA

Category: Cactus
Type: Grass
Attacks: Poison Sting, Leer, Absorb, Growth, Leech Seed, Sand Attack, Pin Missile, Ingrain, Faint Attack, Spikes, Needle Arm, Cotton Spore, Sandstorm
Evolution: >Cacturne
Height: 0.4m/1'4"
Weight: 51.3kg/113lb

120 CACTURNE

Category: Scarecrow
Type: Grass/Dark
Attacks: Poison Sting, Leer, Absorb, Growth, Leech Seed, Sand Attack, Pin Missile, Ingrain, Faint Attack, Spikes, Needle Arm, Cotton Spore, Sandstorm
Evolution: None
Height: 1.3m/4'3"
Weight: 77.4kg/171lb

GAME WINNING ASSIST!

On the way to Lavaridge Town, Ash and his friends took a shortcut through a cave called the Fiery Path. But May's Skitty escaped and attacked some Slugma, and that put them all in danger! The Slugma chased them through the cave. Suddenly Ash spotted a crack in the rock.

"Pikachu, use Iron Tail on it!" he yelled. Pikachu blasted a hole in the rock and they escaped onto the mountainside, then tumbled down a steep hill.

Skitty saw a strange Pokémon and went over to say hello. It was a Numel, and it was fast asleep. Skitty tried some attacks on it, but it just wouldn't wake up. Ash checked his Pokédex. "Numel does not even notice when it is hit," he read. "Its body is filled with hot magma." Just then, a woman walked towards them with a herd of Numel. Her name was Julie and she ran a Numel ranch not far away. She had a Furret who helped her stop the Numel getting lost.

Ash explained that they were travelling to Lavaridge Town.

"If you need a break, come and hang out at my place," Julie offered. "I live nearby."

"That would be great," said Ash. "Thank you!"

They walked back to Julie's ranch and helped her herd the Numel into their pen. But they didn't know they were being watched. Team Rocket was hiding nearby!

"With all that internal magma, Numel can be used instead of ovens and heaters," said James. "Let's catch all of those Numel and sell them!" exclaimed Jessie. "We'll be rich!"

After Julie had fed the Numel, May challenged her to a battle and she accepted.
"Skitty, I choose you!" cried May. "Let's start by watching our opponent's moves closely!"
But Skitty rushed forward, eager to start the battle! Furret ran in circles and Skitty chased it.
"Watch your opponent's movements!" May shouted.
"Furret, stop in your tracks!" yelled Julie. Furret stopped instantly and Skitty charged into it and was sent flying!
"Skitty, use Tackle!" ordered May. But Furret dodged every attack. May didn't know what to do!

"Now is the time to use your Pokédex, May," said Julie. May grabbed her Pokédex and looked up Skitty's attacks. Then she gave a wide grin. "Skitty, use Assist!" she said. Ash frowned – even he had never heard of that one! But he gasped when he saw Skitty using Ember!

"That means Ember and Assist are the same?" Ash wondered. "Skitty, use Assist one more time!" shouted May. This time Skitty used Silver Wind! But Furret slammed Skitty to the ground and the battle was over. May cradled Skitty in her arms. "I had no idea Skitty could use Ember or Silver Wind," said May in surprise.

"That's what Assist attack is all about," Julie explained. "You can use attacks from any of your Pokémon, even if they're not in the battle."

"Awesome!" said Ash. "So Skitty was able to use attacks from May's Torchic and her Beautifly!"

"I used to be a Pokémon coordinator," Julie said. "I'm really impressed with that Skitty of yours, May. Skitty's speed and attacks were right on. With a little practice, you're gonna be tough to beat in contests and battles!" May was very pleased to hear that!

Later that night, when everyone was asleep in bed, something strange started to happen outside. A huge mechanical Numel walked up the hillside towards the ranch. All the Numel were fast asleep in their pen. Long arms reached out of the machine and grabbed the sleeping Numel, dropping them into the belly of the machine. Inside the mechanical Numel, Team Rocket was cackling with laughter. Their plot to steal the Numel was working!

Inside the ranch, Furret and Pikachu sensed that something was wrong. Pikachu woke everyone up and they rushed to the window. They could hardly believe their eyes.

"Someone's stealing the Numel!" gasped May. They rushed outside and saw Jessie, James and Meowth at the controls of the machine.

"Team Rocket!" yelled Ash.

"What do you think you're doing with my Numel?" shouted Julie.

"We don't think, we know!" Jessie sneered. "We're stealing them all."

"Pikachu, Thunderbolt!" Ash ordered. Pikachu's attack hit the machine but it had no effect!

The machine started to leave and Skitty ran to attack it.
"Skitty, no!" yelled May. "Come back!"
She ran after Skitty, but they landed on one of the mechanical arms and got taken
nto the belly of the machine. The others stared in horror as Team Rocket left!
"Team Rocket has my sister!" Max cried.
"They're not going anywhere, I promise," said Ash.
Julie roared up in her truck and they piled in to chase
the thieves.

Inside the belly of the machine, May and Skitty tried to escape. "Skitty, use Tackle on the wall!" said May. Skitty tried, but the attack just bounced off. Then the Numel started to wake up! At the controls, Team Rocket was talking about all the money that would come from selling the Numel. They were stopped by a pounding noise – the Numel were throwing themselves against the side of the machine.

Meowth pressed a button and suddenly water sprinkled onto the Numel, cooling off the magma inside them!

The Numel kept battering the wall, but it was no use – it was made of metal and much too strong. They were starting to get sleepy again because their magma was cooling!

Suddenly May had an idea. "Skitty can use Assist to pull off Ember attack!" she thought. Skitty's Ember attack relit the magma in the Numel. Then they all breathed fire onto the metal walls of the machine!

"It's working!" cried May.

"Hey, did someone turn up the heat?" asked James. It was getting very hot at the controls. Meowth put the water spray on again, but this time Skitty used Double Slap to destroy the sprinklers!

The Numel's fiery breath burned holes in the side of the machine and at last it collapsed and burst into flames. May, Skitty and the Numel escaped just in time!

"That twerpy girl and her Skitty!" raged Jessie as Team Rocket jumped out of the machine.

Ash and his friends skidded up in the truck.
"Prepare for a fight!" Jessie yelled. "Seviper,
let's go!"
"You too, Cacnea!" James cried.
"Seviper, use Poison Tail against that Furret!"
But Julie was ready for them! "Dodge and use
Slam!" she yelled. Seviper was knocked out!
"Cacnea – Needle Arm attack!" ordered James.
"Pikachu, Thunderbolt attack, go!" Ash shouted.
Cacnea was knocked back and Team Rocket
blasted off again!
"We did it, Pikachu!" cheered Ash. The Numel
were safe!

Next morning the friends said goodbye to Julie.

"See that path?" she said. "If you follow it towards that large tree, you'll come to the Ropeway Station. Use it to cross Mount Chimney, then go to Lavaridge Town."

"Thanks for your help!" smiled May, and they waved goodbye to their new friend as they continued on their journey towards Lavaridge Town.

THE END

121 SWABLU

Category: Cotton Bird
Type: Normal/Flying
Attacks: Peck, Growl, Astonish, Sing, Fury Attack, Safeguard, Mist, Take Down, Mirror Move, Refresh, Perish Song
Evolution: >Altaria
Height: 0.4m/1'4"
Weight: 1.2kg/3lb

126 SOLROCK

Category: Meteorite
Type: Rock/Psychic
Attacks: Tackle, Harden, Confusion, Rock Throw, Fire Spin, Psywave, Cosmic Power, Rock Slide, Solarbeam, Explosion
Evolution: None
Height: 1.2m/3'11"
Weight: 154kg/340lb

122 ALTARIA

Category: Humming
Type: Dragon/Flying
Attacks: Peck, Growl, Astonish, Sing, Fury Attack, Safeguard, Mist, Take Down, Dragonbreath, Dragon Dance, Refresh, Perish Song, Sky Attack
Evolution: None
Height: 1.1m/3'7"
Weight: 20.6kg/45lb

127 BARBOACH

Category: Whiskers
Type: Water/Ground
Attacks: Mud Slap, Mud Sport, Water Sport, Water Gun, Magnitude, Amnesia, Rest, Snore, Earthquake, Future Sight, Fissure
Evolution: >Whiscash
Height: 0.4m/1'4"
Weight: 1.9kg/4lb

123 ZANGOOSE

Category: Cat Ferret
Type: Normal
Attacks: Scratch, Leer, Quick Attack, Swords Dance, Fury Cutter, Slash, Pursuit, Crush Claw, Taunt, Detect, False Swipe
Evolution: None
Height: 1.3m/4'3"
Weight: 40.3kg/89lb

128 WHISCASH

Category: Whiskers
Type: Water/Ground
Attacks: Tickle, Mud Slap, Mud Sport, Water Sport, Water Gun, Magnitude, Amnesia, Rest, Snore, Earthquake, Future Sight, Fissure
Evolution: None
Height: 0.9m/2'11"
Weight: 23.6kg/52lb

124 SEVIPER

Category: Fang Snake
Type: Poison
Attacks: Wrap, Lick, Bite, Poison Tail, Screech, Glare, Crunch, Poison Fang, Swagger, Haze
Evolution: None
Height: 2.7m/8'10"
Weight: 52.5kg/116kg

129 CORPHISH

Category: Ruffian
Type: Water
Attacks: Bubble, Harden, Vicegrip, Leer, Bubblebeam, Protect, Knock Off, Taunt, Crabhammer, Swords Dance, Guillotine
Evolution: >Crawdaunt
Height: 0.6m/2'0"
Weight: 11.5kg/25lb

125 LUNATONE

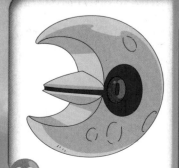

Category: Meteorite
Type: Rock/Psychic
Attacks: Tackle, Harden, Confusion, Rock Throw, Hypnosis, Psywave, Cosmic Power, Psychic, Future Sight, Explosion
Evolution: None
Height: 1m/3'3"
Weight: 168kg/370lb

130 CRAWDAUNT

Category: Rogue
Type: Water/Dark
Attacks: Bubble, Harden, Vicegrip, Leer, Bubblebeam, Protect, Knock Off, Taunt, Crabhammer, Swords Dance, Guillotine
Evolution: None
Height: 1.1m/3'7"
Weight: 32.8kg/72lb

131 BALTOY

Category: Clay Doll
Type: Ground/Psychic
Attacks: Confusion, Harden, Rapid Spin, Mud Slap, Psybeam, Rock Tomb, Selfdestruct, Ancientpower, Sandstorm, Cosmic Power, Explosion
Evolution: >Claydol
Height: 0.5m/1'8"
Weight: 21.5kg/47lb

136 ARMALDO

Category: Plate
Type: Rock/Bug
Attacks: Scratch, Harden, Mud Sport, Water Gun, Metal Claw, Protect, Ancientpower, Fury Cutter, Slash, Rock Blast
Evolution: None
Height: 1.5m/4'11"
Weight: 68.2kg/150lb

132 CLAYDOL

Category: Clay Doll
Type: Ground/Psychic
Attacks: Teleport, Confusion, Harden, Rapid Spin, Mud Slap, Psybeam, Rock Tomb, Selfdestruct, Ancientpower, Sandstom, Hyper Beam, Cosmic Power, Explosion
Evolution: None
Height: 1.5m/4'11"
Weight: 108kg/238lb

137 IGGLYBUFF

Category: Balloon
Type: Normal
Attacks: Sing, Charm, Defence Curl, Pound, Sweet Kiss
Evolution: >Jigglypuff >Wigglytuff
Height: 0.3m/1'0"
Weight: 1kg/2lb

133 LILEEP

Category: Sea Lily
Type: Rock/Grass
Attacks: Astonish, Constrict, Acid, Ingrain, Confuse Ray, Amnesia, Ancientpower, Stockpile, Spit Up, Swallow
Evolution: >Cradily
Height: 1m/3'3"
Weight: 23.8kg/52lb

138 JIGGLYPUFF

Category: Balloon
Type: Normal
Attacks: Sing, Defence Curl, Pound, Disable, Rollout, Doubleslap, Rest, Body Slam, Mimic, Hyper Voice, Double Edge
Evolution: >Wigglytuff
Height: 0.5m/1'8"
Weight: 5.5kg/12lb

134 CRADILY

Category: Barnacle
Type: Rock/Grass
Attacks: Astonish, Constrict, Acid, Ingrain, Confuse Ray, Amnesia, Ancientpower, Stockpile, Spit Up, Swallow
Evolution: None
Height: 1.5m/4'11"
Weight: 60.4/133lb

139 WIGGLYTUFF

Category: Balloon
Type: Normal
Attacks: Sing, Disable, Defence Curl, Doubleslap
Evolution: None
Height: 1m/3'3"
Weight: 12kg/26lb

135 ANORITH

Category: Old Shrimp
Type: Rock/Bug
Attacks: Scratch, Harden, Mud Sport, Water Gun, Metal Claw, Protect, Ancientpower, Fury Cutter, Slash, Rock Blast
Evolution: >Armaldo
Height: 0.7m/2'4"
Weight: 12.5kg/28lb

140 FEEBAS

Category: Fish
Type: Water
Attacks: Splash, Tackle, Flail
Evolution: >Milotic
Height: 0.6m/2'0"
Weight: 7.4kg/16lb

 141 MILOTIC

Category: Tender
Type: Water
Attacks: Water Gun, Wrap, Water Sport, Refresh, Water Pulse, Twister, Recover, Rain Dance, Hydro Pump, Attract, Safeguard
Evolution: None
Height: 6.2m/20'4"
Weight: 162kg/357lb

 146 SHUPPET

Category: Puppet
Type: Ghost
Attacks: Knock Off, Screech, Night Shade, Curse, Spite, Will-O-Wisp, Faint Attack, Shadow Ball, Snatch, Grudge
Evolution: >Banette
Height: 0.6m/2'0"
Weight: 2.3kg/5lb

 142 CASTFORM

Category: Weather
Type: Normal
Attacks: Tackle, Water Gun, Ember, Powder Snow, Rain Dance, Sunny Day, Hail, Weather Ball
Evolution: None
Height: 0.3m/1'0"
Weight: 0.8kg/2lb

 147 BANETTE

Category: Marionette
Type: Ghost
Attacks: Knock Off, Screech, Night Shade, Curse, Spite, Will-O-Wisp, Faint Attack, Shadow Ball, Snatch, Grudge
Evolution: None
Height: 1.1m/3'7"
Weight: 12.5kg/28lb

 143 STARYU

Category: Star Shape
Type: Water
Attacks: Tackle, Harden, Water Gun, Rapid Spin, Recover, Camouflage, Swift, Bubblebeam, Minimise, Light Screen, Cosmic Power, Hydro Pump
Evolution: >Starmie
Height: 0.8m/2'7"
Weight: 34.5kg/76lb

 148 DUSKULL

Category: Requiem
Type: Ghost
Attacks: Leer, Night Shade, Disable, Foresight, Astonish, Confuse Ray, Pursuit, Curse, Will-O-Wisp, Mean Look, Future Sight
Evolution: >Dusclops
Height: 0.8m/2'7"
Weight: 15kg/33lb

 144 STARMIE

Category: Mysterious
Type: Water/Psychic
Attacks: Water Gun, Rapid Spin, Recover, Swift, Confuse Ray
Evolution: None
Height: 1.1m/3'7"
Weight: 80kg/176lb

 149 DUSCLOPS

Category: Beckon
Type: Ghost
Attacks: Bind, Leer, Night Shade, Disable, Foresight, Astonish, Confuse Ray, Pursuit, Curse, Shadow Punch, Will-O-Wisp, Mean Look, Future Sight
Evolution: None
Height: 1.6m/5'3"
Weight: 30.6kg/67lb

 145 KECLEON

Category: Colour Swap
Type: Normal
Attacks: Thief, Tail Whip, Astonish, Lick, Scratch, Bind, Faint Attack, Fury Swipes, Psybeam, Screech, Slash, Substitute, Ancientpower
Evolution: None
Height: 1m/3'3"
Weight: 22kg/49lb

 150 TROPIUS

Category: Fruit
Type: Grass/Flying
Attacks: Leer, Gust, Growth, Razor Leaf, Stomp, Sweet Scent, Whirlwind, Magical Leaf, Body Slam, Solarbeam, Synthesis
Evolution: None
Height: 2m/6'7"
Weight: 100kg/221lb

151 CHIMECHO

Category: Wind Chime
Type: Psychic
Attacks: Wrap, Growl, Astonish, Confusion, Take Down, Uproar, Yawn, Psywave, Double Edge, Heal Bell, Safeguard, Psychic
Evolution: None
Height: 0.6m/2'0"
Weight: 1kg/2lb

152 ABSOL

Category: Disaster
Type: Dark
Attacks: Scratch, Leer, Taunt, Quick Attack, Razor Wind, Bite, Swords Dance, Double Team, Slash, Future Sight, Perish Song
Evolution: None
Height: 1.2m/3'11"
Weight: 47kg/104lb

153 VULPIX

Category: Fox
Type: Fire
Attacks: Ember, Tail Whip, Roar, Quick Attack, Will-O-Wisp, Confuse Ray, Imprison, Flamethrower, Safeguard, Grudge, Fire Spin
Evolution: >Ninetales
Height: 0.6m/2'0"
Weight: 9.9kg/22lb

154 NINETALES

Category: Fox
Type: Fire
Attacks: Ember, Quick Attack, Confuse Ray, Safeguard, Fire Spin
Evolution: None
Height: 1.1m/3'7"
Weight: 19.9kg/44lb

155 PICHU

Category: Tiny Mouse
Type: Electric
Attacks: Thundershock, Charm, Tail Whip, Thunder Wave, Sweet Kiss
Evolution: >Pikachu >Raichu
Height: 0.3m/1'0"
Weight: 2kg/4lb

156 PIKACHU

Category: Mouse
Type: Electric
Attacks: Thundershock, Growl, Tail Whip, Thunder Wave, Quick Attack, Double Team, Slam, Thunderbolt, Agility, Thunder, Light Screen
Evolution: >Raichu
Height: 0.4m/1'4"
Weight: 6kg/13lb

157 RAICHU

Category: Mouse
Type: Electric
Attacks: Thundershock, Tail Whip, Quick Attack, Thunderbolt
Evolution: None
Height: 0.8m/2'7"
Weight: 30kg/66lb

158 PSYDUCK

Category: Duck
Type: Water
Attacks: Water Sport, Scratch, Tail Whip, Disable, Confusion, Screech, Psych Up, Fury Swipes, Hydro Pump
Evolution: >Golduck
Height: 0.8m/2'7"
Weight: 19.6kg/43lb

159 GOLDUCK

Category: Duck
Type: Water
Attacks: Water Sport, Scratch, Tail Whip, Disable, Confusion, Screech, Psych Up, Fury Swipes, Hydro Pump
Evolution: None
Height: 1.7m/5'7"
Weight: 76.6kg/169lb

160 WYNAUT

Category: Bright
Type: Psychic
Attacks: Splash, Charm, Encore, Counter, Mirror Coat, Safeguard, Destiny Bond
Evolution: >Wobbuffet
Height: 0.6m/2'0"
Weight: 14kg/31lb

THE MAUVILLE CITY MARATHON

Join the race to complete the Hoenn gym circuit. But watch out for the other teams trying to stop you along the way!

OLDALE TOWN

You fall into Jessie's pitfall trap! Miss a go

Your Pokéballs have been stolen! Go back to start

Brock's cooking gives you an energy boost. Go forward 2 spaces

You win a battle! Dash forward 3 spaces

SLATEPORT CITY GYM

PETALBURG CITY GYM

You're late! Hurry forward 2 spaces

RUSTBORO CITY GYM

You win a battle! Dash forward 3 spaces

Team Rocket is lost. Jump forward 1 space

86

A game for 2 or more players.
You will need: a marker for each player and 2 dice.

How to play:
- Flip a coin to decide who goes first.
- Throw the dice and move your marker along the trail.
- Check out the instructions where you have landed and do what they say!
- The first trainer to reach Mauville City Gym is the winner!

DEWFORD ISLAND GYM

You challenge the local gym leader. Have another go

You stop to help a wounded Pokémon. Miss a go

You catch a Taillow! Have another go

You bump into Team Magma. Turn back 3 spaces

You take a wrong turning. Fall back 2 spaces

Team Aqua attacks! Go back 1 space

MAUVILLE CITY GYM

FIGHT FOR THE METEORITE!

"Guys, come on!" shouted Ash. "We're gonna miss the cable car!" They had finally reached Ropeway Station at the foot of Mount Chimney. They piled into the cable car, followed by three other passengers. The cable car doors shut and the car began to move up the side of the mountain.

The other three passengers sniggered. It was Team Rocket in disguise!

"Look how close we are to them!" giggled Jessie.

"From this range it'll be a cinch grabbing Pikachu," grinned Meowth. They walked over and smiled at Ash.

"We're the official tour guide crew," said Jessie.

"We didn't order that," Max frowned as a red helicopter sped past the cable car.

Up on Mount Chimney, a scientist called Professor Cosmo was searching the area with a scanner. At last he saw what he was looking for. "There it is! I thought it was a meteor that hit and I was *right*!" Behind him the red helicopter landed on a rock. The ramp lowered and Team Magma appeared.

"We're here for that meteorite, Professor, and you're going to give it to us!" ordered Field Commander Tabitha.

The Professor clutched the meteorite close to him. "No way!"

In the cable car Jessie was still pretending to be a tour guide when another huge helicopter passed them. "They're both heading for the mountaintop," said May. "Something's going on up there," Brock added. The second helicopter landed next to the cable car station on top of the mountain. It was Team Aqua! They attacked the cable car operators and the cable car stopped, dangling high above the ground.

Jessie started to panic.

"I don't know how to get off this thing!" she screamed.

"Aren't you the guide?" asked Max.

"Aren't you trained for emergencies?" May added.

"Something's a little bit fishy," said Brock.

"Yeah, who *are* you guys?" Max frowned.

"Glad you asked!" cackled Jessie, pulling off her disguise.

"Team Rocket!" Ash yelled.

On the mountaintop, Team Magma was closing in on the Professor.
"I need this meteor for my research – you can never have it!" shouted the Professor.
"That rock holds powers far beyond what you could ever imagine!" Tabitha sneered. At that moment Team Aqua appeared behind them!
"A pleasure to see you again, Field Commander Tabitha," hissed Shelley, the leader of Team Aqua. She wanted the meteorite too. But while the teams prepared to battle, the Professor ran off with the meteorite!

In the cable car, Ash found a rope hook under one of the seats. They all crawled out onto the roof. Luckily the car had stopped close to one of the towers. Ash threw one end of the rope to the tower, where it hooked on tightly. Brock tied the other end to the car.
"We're gonna crawl across," said Ash. "From the tower we'll climb down."
Ash started to crawl across, with Pikachu clinging to his back. The others watched nervously as he inched his way along the thin rope.

Then Team Rocket panicked! They thought they were going to be left behind, so they all jumped onto the rope. The extra weight was too much for the rope – it snapped and sent them all swinging through the air! Team Rocket hung from the end attached to the cable car, while Ash crashed into the tower and clung on. He looked back at his friends.
"I'll get some help and come back for you!" he called.

On the mountaintop, Team Magma was starting to win the fight. Shelley could see that they were going to be beaten.
"Retreat and regroup!" she ordered, and Team Aqua backed off.
"Prepare the system!" Tabitha told Team Magma. "I want it fully operational!"

The scared Professor was running for his life, clutching the meteorite. Ash had just reached the top of the mountain when the Professor charged straight into him and knocked them both down! "Sorry!" gasped the Professor. "What were you running from?" asked Ash, struggling to his feet.

"I'm being chased by a dozen strange strangers!" panted the professor. He and Ash hid behind a rock as the chasers ran past.

Ash's eyes opened wide. "Team Magma!" he exclaimed. "I don't know much about 'em, but I know they're up to no good!"

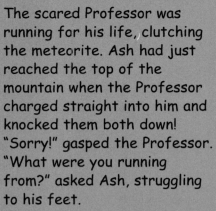

The Professor gulped. "My name's Cosmo," he said. "I've been studying asteroids and meteorites for years. This is a meteorite. Obviously I'm not the only one who wants it. I can't figure out why they want it so much."

"Does it have some power they could use for something bad?" asked Ash.

"Possibly, but I don't know. All I want is to study it."

Professor Cosmo explained where meteorites came from. Ash and Pikachu were amazed to be able to touch something that had come from outer space. But suddenly the meteorite was snatched from his hands. It was Team Magma! They ran off with it and Ash sprang to his feet.

"Come on, let's go get it back!" he cried.

Ash's friends were still hanging in mid air. The cable car was swinging in the high wind.
"I'm scared!" cried Max.
"Don't worry," May said. "I'll bet Ash is on his way back here right now." But Ash was doing something even more dangerous!

"Bring the laser online now and calibrate," ordered Tabitha.
Team Magma placed the meteorite into the laser and aimed the laser at the lava flow in the mouth of the volcano. Ash and Professor Cosmo watched from their hiding place.
"If we don't stop this, that lava could come rushing out!" gasped the Professor.

"Soon the very energy of the earth will be in our control!" Tabitha laughed.

Suddenly Professor Cosmo appeared on a rock above Team Magma. "Hey! Give me back that meteorite!" he yelled.

As Team Magma chased the Professor, Ash rushed over to the laser. The meteorite was glowing red inside. He tried to open the machine, but it had been sealed shut.

"Pikachu, Thunderbolt it!" cried Ash. But Pikachu's attack caused an overload of power in the laser. Team Magma lost control of the machine and everyone was in danger range!

"The meteorite!" cried Ash.
"Better that no one has it than to see it used for evil!" shouted Professor Cosmo. He shoved the laser into the bubbling lava far below. It was destroyed!
"Let's move out!" yelled Tabitha furiously.
From a nearby rock, Team Aqua was watching everything.
"Any loss for Team Magma is a win for us!" grinned Shelley.

The two evil teams took off in their helicopters and Ash and the Professor headed for the cable car station. They soon freed the engineers and brought the cable car safely into the station.
"I'm glad to be on solid ground!" said Max.
Team Rocket was plotting again.
"Let's go get Pikachu!" whispered Jessie. But before they could move, the rock they were standing on broke away! Team Rocket tumbled back down the mountain!

"Just follow this mountain road and it'll lead you right to Lavaridge Town," Professor Cosmo told Ash and his friends. They had had a dangerous adventure but, as they waved goodbye, Ash's thoughts were only on his battle in Lavaridge Town!

THE END

161 WOBBUFFET

Category: Patient
Type: Psychic
Attacks: Counter, Mirror Coat, Safeguard, Destiny Bond
Evolution: None
Height: 1.3m/4'3"
Weight: 28.5kg/63lb

166 DONPHAN

Category: Armour
Type: Ground
Attacks: Odour Sleuth, Horn Attack, Growl, Defence Curl, Flail, Fury Attack, Rollout, Rapid Spin, Earthquake
Evolution: None
Height: 1.1m/3'7"
Weight: 120kg/265lb

162 NATU

Category: Tiny Bird
Type: Psychic/Flying
Attacks: Peck, Leer, Night Shade, Teleport, Wish, Future Sight, Confuse Ray, Psychic
Evolution: >Xatu
Height: 0.2m/0'8"
Weight: 2kg/4lb

167 PINSIR

Category: Stag Beetle
Type: Bug
Attacks: Vicegrip, Focus Energy, Bind, Seismic Toss, Harden, Revenge, Brick Break, Guillotine, Submission, Swords Dance
Evolution: None
Height: 1.5m/4'11"
Weight: 55kg/121lb

163 XATU

Category: Mystic
Type: Psychic/Flying
Attacks: Peck, Leer, Night Shade, Teleport, Wish, Future Sight, Confuse Ray, Psychic
Evolution: None
Height: 1.5m/4'11"
Weight: 15kg/33lb

168 HERACROSS

Category: Single Horn
Type: Bug/Fighting
Attacks: Tackle, Leer, Horn Attack, Endure, Fury Attack, Brick Break, Counter, Take Down, Reversal, Megahorn
Evolution: None
Height: 1.5m/4'11"
Weight: 54kg/119lb

164 GIRAFARIG

Category: Long Neck
Type: Normal/Psychic
Attacks: Tackle, Growl, Astonish, Confusion, Stomp, Odour Sleuth, Agility, Baton Pass, Psybeam, Crunch
Evolution: None
Height: 1.5m/4'11"
Weight: 41.5kg/92lb

169 RHYHORN

Category: Spikes
Type: Ground/Rock
Attacks: Horn Attack, Tail Whip, Stomp, Fury Attack, Scary Face, Rock Blast, Horn Drill, Take Down, Earthquake, Megahorn
Evolution: >Rhydon
Height: 1m/3'3"
Weight: 115kg/254lb

165 PHANPY

Category: Long Nose
Type: Ground
Attacks: Odour Sleuth, Tackle, Growl, Defence Curl, Flail, Take Down, Rollout, Endure, Double Edge
Evolution: >Donphan
Height: 0.5m/1'8"
Weight: 33.5kg/74lb

170 RHYDON

Category: Drill
Type: Ground/Rock
Attacks: Horn Attack, Tail Whip, Stomp, Fury Attack, Scary Face, Rock Blast, Horn Drill, Take Down, Earthquake, Megahorn
Evolution: None
Height: 1.9m/6'3"
Weight: 120kg/265lb

171 SNORUNT

Category: Snow Hat
Type: Ice
Attacks: Powder Snow, Leer, Double Team, Bite, Icy Wind, Headbutt, Protect, Crunch, Ice Beam, Hail, Blizzard
Evolution: >Glalie
Height: 0.7m/2'4"
Weight: 16.8kg/37lb

172 GLALIE

Category: Face
Type: Ice
Attacks: Powder Snow, Leer, Double Team, Bite, Icy Wind, Headbutt, Protect, Crunch, Ice Beam, Hail, Blizzard, Sheer Cold
Evolution: None
Height: 1.5m/4'11"
Weight: 256.5kg/566lb

173 SPHEAL

Category: Clap
Type: Ice/Water
Attacks: Powder Snow, Growl, Water Gun, Encore, Ice Ball, Body Slam, Aurora Beam, Hail, Rest, Snore, Blizzard, Sheer Cold
Evolution: >Sealeo >Walrein
Height: 0.8m/2'7"
Weight: 39.5kg/87lb

174 SEALEO

Category: Ball Roll
Type: Ice/Water
Attacks: Powder Snow, Growl, Water Gun, Encore, Ice Ball, Body Slam, Aurora Beam, Hail, Rest, Snore, Blizzard, Sheer Cold
Evolution: >Walrein
Height: 1.1m/3'7"
Weight: 87.6kg/193lb

175 WALREIN

Category: Ice Break
Type: Ice/Water
Attacks: Powder Snow, Growl, Water Gun, Encore, Ice Ball, Body Slam, Aurora Beam, Hail, Rest, Snore, Blizzard, Sheer Cold
Evolution: None
Height: 1.4m/4'7"
Weight: 150.6kg/332lb

176 CLAMPERL

Category: Bivalve
Type: Water
Attacks: Clamp, Water Gun, Whirlpool, Iron Defence
Evolution: >Huntail >Gorebyss
Height: 0.4m/1'4"
Weight: 52.5/116lb

177 HUNTAIL

Category: Deep Sea
Type: Water
Attacks: Whirlpool, Bite, Screech, Water Pulse, Scary Face, Crunch, Baton Pass, Hydro Pump
Evolution: >Gorebyss
Height: 1.7m/5'7"
Weight: 27kg/60lb

178 GOREBYSS

Category: South Sea
Type: Water
Attacks: Whirlpool, Confusion, Agility, Water Pulse, Amnesia, Psychic, Baton Pass, Hydro Pump
Evolution: None
Height: 1.8m/5'11"
Weight: 22.6kg/50lb

179 RELICANTH

Category: Longevity
Type: Water/Rock
Attacks: Tackle, Harden, Water Gun, Rock Tomb, Yawn, Take Down, Mud Sport, Ancientpower, Rest, Double Edge, Hydro Pump
Evolution: None
Height: 1m/3'3"
Weight: 23.4kg/52lb

180 CORSOLA

Category: Coral
Type: Water/Rock
Attacks: Tackle, Harden, Bubble, Recover, Refresh, Bubblebeam, Spike Cannon, Rock Blast, Mirror Coat, Ancientpower
Evolution: None
Height: 0.6m/2'0"
Weight: 5kg/11lb

181 CHINCHOU

Category: Angler
Type: Water/Electric
Attacks: Bubble, Thunder Wave, Supersonic, Flail, Water Gun, Spark, Confuse Ray, Take Down, Hydro Pump, Charge
Evolution: >Lanturn
Height: 0.5m/1'8"
Weight: 12kg/26lb

186 KINGDRA

Category: Dragon
Type: Water/Dragon
Attacks: Bubble, Smokescreen, Leer, Water Gun, Twister, Agility, Hydro Pump, Dragon Dance
Evolution: None
Height: 1.8m/5'11"
Weight: 152kg/335lb

182 LANTURN

Category: Light
Type: Water/Electric
Attacks: Bubble, Thunder Wave, Supersonic, Flail, Water Gun, Spark, Confuse Ray, Take Down, Hydro Pump, Charge
Evolution: None
Height: 1.2m3'11"
Weight: 22.5kg/50lb

187 BAGON

Category: Rock Head
Type: Dragon
Attacks: Rage, Bite, Leer, Headbutt, Focus Energy, Ember, Dragonbreath, Scary Face, Crunch, Dragon Claw, Double Edge
Evolution: >Shelgon >Salamence
Height: 0.6m/2'0"
Weight: 42.1kg/93lb

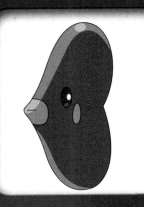

183 LUVDISC

Category: Rendezvous
Type: Water
Attacks: Tackle, Charm, Water Gun, Agility, Take Down, Sweet Kiss, Attract, Flail, Safeguard
Evolution: None
Height: 0.6m/2'0"
Weight: 8.7kg/19lb

188 SHELGON

Category: Endurance
Type: Dragon
Attacks: Rage, Bite, Leer, Headbutt, Focus Energy, Ember, Protect, Dragonbreath, Scary Face, Crunch, Dragon Claw, Double Edge
Evolution: >Salamence
Height: 1.1m/3'7"
Weight: 110.5kg/244lb

184 HORSEA

Category: Dragon
Type: Water
Attacks: Bubble, Smokescreen, Leer, Water Gun, Twister, Agility, Hydro Pump, Dragon Dance
Evolution: >Seadra >Kingdra
Height: 0.4m/1'4"
Weight: 8kg/18lb

189 SALAMENCE

Category: Dragon
Type: Dragon/Flying
Attacks: Rage, Bite, Leer, Headbutt, Focus Energy, Ember, Protect, Dragonbreath, Scary Face, Fly, Crunch, Dragon Claw, Double Edge
Evolution: None
Height: 1.5m/4'11"
Weight: 102.6kg/226lb

185 SEADRA

Category: Dragon
Type: Water
Attacks: Bubble, Smokescreen, Leer, Water Gun, Twister, Agility, Hydro Pump, Dragon Dance
Evolution: >Kingdra
Height: 1.2m/3'11"
Weight: 25kg/55lb

190 BELDUM

Category: Iron Ball
Type: Steel/Psychic
Attacks: Take Down
Evolution: >Metang >Metagross
Height: 0.6m/2'0"
Weight: 95.2kg/210lb

191 METANG

Category: Iron Claw
Type: Steel/Psychic
Attacks: Take Down, Confusion, Metal Claw, Scary Face, Pursuit, Psychic, Iron Defence, Meteor Mash, Agiliity, Hyper Beam
Evolution: >Metagross
Height: 1.2m/3'11"
Weight: 202.5kg/447lb

192 METAGROSS

Category: Iron Leg
Type: Steel/Psychic
Attacks: Take Down, Confusion, Metal Claw, Scary Face, Pursuit, Psychic, Iron Defence, Meteor Mash, Agiliity, Hyper Beam
Evolution: None
Height: 1.6m/5'3"
Weight: 550kg/1213lb

193 REGIROCK

Category: Rock Peak
Type: Rock
Attacks: Explosion, Rock Throw, Curse, Superpower, Ancientpower, Iron Defence, Zap Cannon, Lock On, Hyper Beam
Evolution: None
Height: 1.7m/5'7"
Weight: 230kg/507lb

194 REGICE

Category: Iceberg
Type: Ice
Attacks: Explosion, Icy Wind, Curse, Superpower, Ancientpower, Amnesia, Zap Cannon, Lock On, Hyper Beam
Evolution: None
Height: 1.8m/5'11"
Weight: 175kg/386lb

195 REGISTEEL

Category: Iron
Type: Steel
Attacks: Explosion, Metal Claw, Curse, Superpower, Ancientpower, Iron Defence, Amnesia, Zap Cannon, Lock On, Hyper Beam
Evolution: None
Height: 1.9m/6'3"
Weight: 205kg/452lb

196 LATIAS

Category: Eon
Type: Dragon/Psychic
Attacks: Psywave, Wish, Helping Hand, Safeguard, Dragonbreath, Water Sport, Refresh, Mist Ball, Psychic, Recover, Charm
Evolution: None
Height: 1.4m/4'7"
Weight: 40kg/88lb

197 LATIOS

Category: Eon
Type: Dragon/Psychic
Attacks: Psywave, Memento, Helping Hand, Safeguard, Dragonbreath, Protect, Refresh, Luster Purge, Psychic, Recover, Dragon Dance
Evolution: None
Height: 2m/6'7"
Weight: 60kg/132lb

198 KYOGRE

Category: Sea Basin
Type: Water
Attacks: Water Pulse, Scary Face, Ancientpower, Body Slam, Calm Mind, Ice Beam, Hydro Pump, Rest, Sheer Cold, Double Edge, Water Spout
Evolution: None
Height: 4.5m/14'9"
Weight: 352kg/776lb

199 GROUDON

Category: Continent
Type: Ground
Attacks: Mud Shot, Scary Face, Ancientpower, Slash, Bulk Up, Earthquake, Fire Blast, Rest, Fissure. Solarbeam, Eruption
Evolution: None
Height: 3.5m/11'6"
Weight: 950kg/2095lb

200 RAYQUAZA

Category: Sky High
Type: Dragon/Flying
Attacks: Twister, Scary Face, Ancientpower, Dragon Claw, Dragon Dance, Crunch, Fly, Rest, Extremespeed, Outrage, Hyper Beam
Evolution: None
Height: 7m/23'0"
Weight: 206.5kg/455lb

Wordsearch pg 13

Q	W	E	P	I	K	A	C	H	U
R	T	Y	I	U	T	C	I	T	O
X	A	M	K	P	R	I	A	W	S
D	F	G	D	H	E	H	J	O	N
B	L	Z	U	X	E	C	C	E	N
R	V	B	M	I	C	R	N	M	E
O	M	Q	S	W	K	O	E	R	O
C	T	S	Y	M	O	T	U	I	H
K	E	O	A	J	A	M	E	S	J
J	P	Y	A	S	D	F	A	G	H

Evolution Exam pg 36

A - 3
B - 1
C - 5
D - 2
E - 4

Odd Pokemon Out pg 36

Group 1 - C
Group 2 - A
Group 3 - C

Crossword pg 59